The Magic Tile

Written by

SUZANNE MUIR

Illustrated by

ANTHONY BRENNAN

MINA

HAYTHAM

IBN BATTUTA

AL-RASHID

SALADIN

KING RICHARD

SINBAD

REAL PEOPLE IN HISTORY

IBN BATTUTA (1304–1368): A famous Muslim traveller who wrote a book about his travels and the people he met.

HARUN AL-RASHID (764–809): Chief ruler of the Abbasid Empire. He was known for his grand and beautiful palace in the ancient city of Baghdad.

SALADIN (1138–1193): A great Muslim ruler, he led his army against the Crusaders who invaded Jerusalem.

KING RICHARD THE LIONHEART (1157–1199): This King of England led the Crusaders to capture the Holy Land from the Muslims.

FICTIONAL CHARACTERS

HAYTHAM: A nine-year-old Muslim boy in this story. He is named after Ibn al-Haytham, a scientist who studied light and rainbows.

MINA: Haytham's twin sister. She has wonderful adventures with her brother.

SINBAD: An exciting character from *The Arabian Nights*.

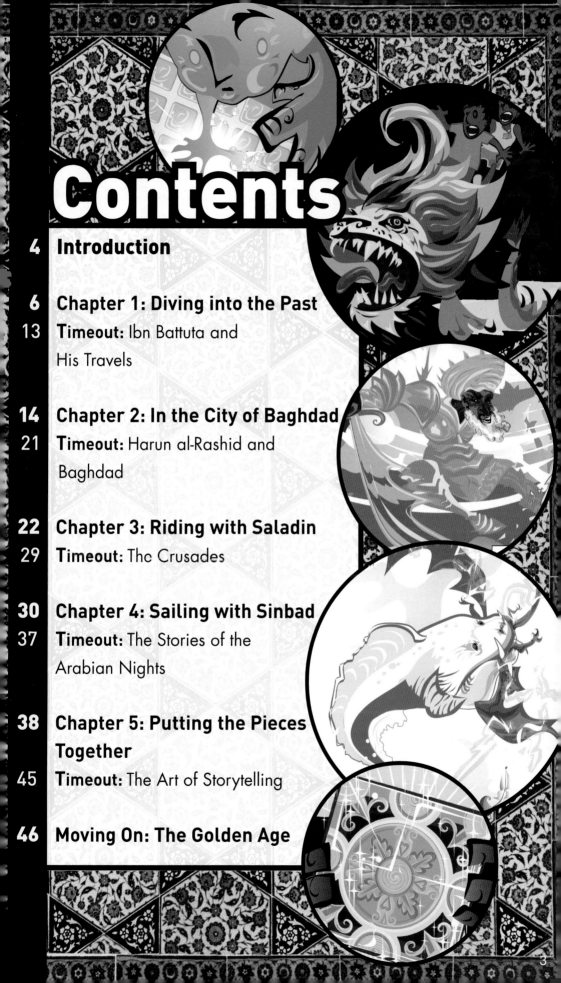

Contents

Defenders of the Muslim Holy Lands

The medieval age lasted almost 1000 years from 500–1500. In Europe, it was a time of knights and castles, of holy wars, and the Black Death.

Just next door to Europe, there was the Abbasid Empire. This empire stretched from modern-day Spain in the west to present-day Indonesia in the east. There were over 40 different cultural groups within the empire. They were united by their common religion — Islam.

Mosque

500 >>	622 >>	750 >>	764 >>	1096 >>
The start of the Middle Ages in Europe.	Muhammad introduces the religion of Islam to Arabia.	The Golden Age of Islam begins.	Harun al-Rashid is born in Baghdad.	The start of the Crusades in Europe.

The Abbasid Empire was very wealthy. People had beautiful gardens and running water in their homes. In the cities, there were busy marketplaces. Trade flourished with China, Africa, and Europe.

It was an exciting time of new inventions and learning in schools and universities. Famous Muslim explorers travelled the world. Many important things that we use today were invented by medieval Muslims. Some examples are cheques, algebra, and even sherbet.

It's no wonder that this period is known as the Golden Age of Islam.

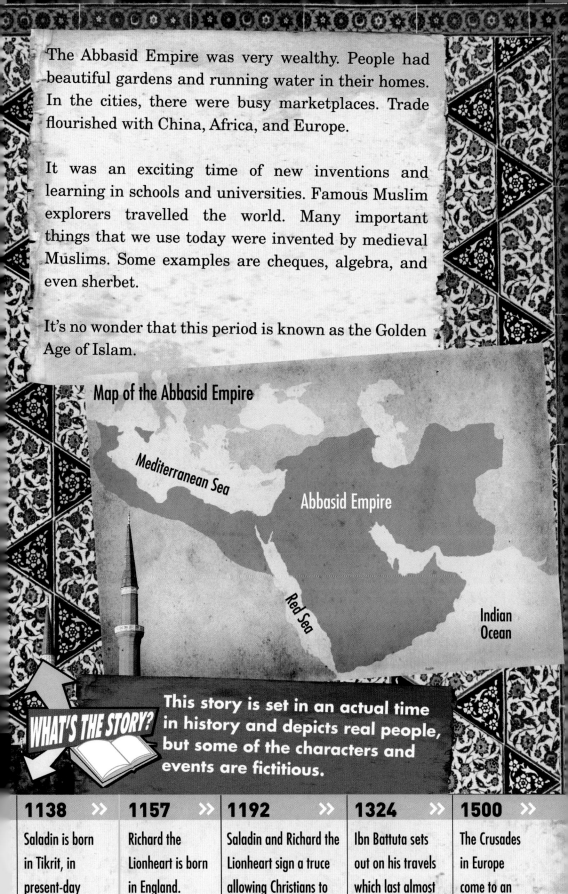

Map of the Abbasid Empire

Mediterranean Sea

Abbasid Empire

Red Sea

Indian Ocean

WHAT'S THE STORY? This story is set in an actual time in history and depicts real people, but some of the characters and events are fictitious.

1138 »	1157 »	1192 »	1324 »	1500 »
Saladin is born in Tikrit, in present-day Iraq.	Richard the Lionheart is born in England.	Saladin and Richard the Lionheart sign a truce allowing Christians to visit Jerusalem.	Ibn Battuta sets out on his travels which last almost 30 years.	The Crusades in Europe come to an end.

HAYTHAM TOUCHES THE SHINING OBJECT. SUDDENLY, THE BOTTOM OF THE POOL OPENS INTO A TUNNEL.
WHOA! WHAT'S THIS PLACE?
MINA LEADS THE WAY.
THIS IS AMAZING! IT'S SOME KIND OF TUNNEL. I HOPE IT LEADS SOME-WHERE EXCITING.
THEY POP UP IN AN OASIS - A PLACE WITH WATER AND TREES - IN THE DESERT.
PTEWEEET
IT SPAT ON ME!
EWWW! GROSS!

MINA AND HAYTHAM RIDE WITH IBN BATTUTA. THEY STOP TO STAY WITH A BEDOUIN TRIBE AND SLEEP IN A TENT UNDER THE STARS. IBN BATTUTA TELLS THEM ABOUT HIS TRAVELS FROM SPAIN TO CHINA.

THE NEXT DAY, THEY ARRIVE AT THE CITY OF TIMBUKTU.

HAYTHAM, DO YOU HEAR THAT NOISE?

YEAH, IT SOUNDS LIKE HORSES – LOTS OF HORSES.

ROBBERS! CHILDREN, YOU MUST RUN. IF THE ROBBERS STEAL THE TILE TO THE PORTAL, YOU'LL BE STUCK IN THIS TIME FOREVER. GO TOWARD THE CITY. YOU'LL FIND WATER THERE.

DANGER!

THANKS FOR ALL YOUR HELP, IBN BATTUTA.

QUICKLY, HAYTHAM. RUN!

SALAAM, CHILDREN.

Ibn Battuta and His Travels

Ibn Battuta was a famous Muslim traveller of the Middle Ages. As a young man, he made a journey to Mecca, the birthplace of the Prophet Muhammad. After Mecca, he just kept going — for almost 30 years! He visited places in China, Southeast Asia, India, and Africa. Ibn Battuta wrote about his travels in a book called *Rihla*, meaning "travels."

Like others in his time, Ibn Battuta travelled on camels in the deserts. Camels are known as "ships of the desert." They can go without food and water for days. They drink whenever they can — up to 100 litres in 10 minutes! And they store fat in their humps. They also have nostrils that they can close up during sandstorms.

Ibn Battuta

India

China

Africa

13

Chapter 2: In the City of Baghdad

IT IS AROUND 800 CE. THE MYSTERIOUS TILE HAS LED THE CHILDREN BACK IN TIME.

THEY ARE NOW AT THE PALACE OF CALIPH HARUN AL-RASHID AND HIS WIFE, QUEEN ZUBAIDA.

AHHH! IT'S GOING TO EAT US!

RELAX. IT'S JUST GETTING A DRINK. LOOK, HAYTHAM! LOOK AT THAT BUILDING!

THE CALIPH'S PALACE IS GUARDED BY 100 LIONS AND SIX ELEPHANTS.

WHOA. WHERE ARE YOU TAKING US?

I RECOGNIZE THIS PALACE. WE'RE AT THE COURT OF CALIPH HARUN AL-RASHID IN BAGHDAD. WE'RE IN THE GOLDEN AGE OF MUSLIM HISTORY.

A PALACE GUARD IS SURPRISED TO FIND AN ELEPHANT BEHIND HIM WITH THE CHILDREN.

OH, GOOD. YOU MUST BE THE CHILDREN SENT TO HELP ME.

LOOK AT WHAT THE LION IS WEARING!

WHAT A BEAUTIFUL COLLAR! I'VE NEVER SEEN ANYTHING LIKE IT.

AN OLD WOMAN GAVE IT TO QUEEN ZUBAIDA. SHE SAID THE OLDEST ROYAL LION SHOULD WEAR IT. BUT SINCE WE PUT THE COLLAR ON THE LION, IT HAS BEEN ACTING STRANGELY ...

... AND NO ONE CAN GET NEAR THE LION TO TAKE IT OFF.

WELL, LET US TRY. WE'RE GOOD WITH ANIMALS.

JUST REMEMBER NOT TO GET TOO CLOSE. IT MAY EAT YOU UP.

Harun al-Rashid and Baghdad

Court of Harun al-Rashid

Harun al-Rashid was the caliph (chief ruler) of the Abbasid Empire from 786–809. He was a ruler of great courage and skill. He became caliph when he was not yet 21 years old!

Medieval Muslim rulers lived in grand palaces with flower gardens and fountains, silk curtains, and fine furniture. Harun al-Rashid's palace in Baghdad was more elegant than any before it.

Harun al-Rashid encouraged learning in his empire. His wife, Queen Zubaida, was well-known for her love of the arts. Baghdad — the capital city — had universities, libraries, hospitals, zoos, and observatories for viewing the stars.

Baghdad was famous for its marketplaces. Merchants from many different lands sold luxurious goods like leather, glass, perfume, spices, and ceramic tiles. Storytellers, snake charmers, and fire eaters entertained the shoppers as they walked through the markets.

IT IS AROUND 1190 CE, ON THE BANKS OF THE RED SEA NEAR JERUSALEM.

OH WOW! ARE WE IN A BATTLE? THAT'S WHAT I LIKE MOST ABOUT MEDIEVAL TIMES.

I WONDER IF WE'LL MEET IBN SINA. HE WAS A FAMOUS DOCTOR OF THIS TIME. HE INVENTED STITCHES TO CLOSE WOUNDS.

I CAN'T BELIEVE MY EYES. DO YOU KNOW WHO THAT IS?

I HAVE NO IDEA. TELL ME.

CHILDREN, JUST OVER THAT RIDGE IS THE FIERCEST KING IN EUROPE – RICHARD THE LIONHEART. HE AND HIS MEN HAVE TRIED TO CAPTURE JERUSALEM, THE HOLY CITY, FROM THE MUSLIMS MANY TIMES.

ARE WE GOING TO FIGHT HIM? CAN I TRY ONE OF YOUR SWORDS?

YOU KNOW WE'RE NOT ALLOWED TO PLAY WITH WEAPONS. WE'LL BE IN TROUBLE IF MOM FINDS OUT!

WELL, WE'RE IN THE MIDDLE AGES, AND THIS IS A FAMOUS BATTLE. I THINK SHE'D UNDERSTAND.

CHILDREN, I HAVE A JOB FOR YOU. THERE IS SOMETHING VERY IMPORTANT IN THIS BOX. PRESENT IT TO KING RICHARD.

YES, MR. SALADIN.

THEY SNEAK PAST THE SLEEPING SOLDIERS.

26

A WELCOME GIFT.

THE TILE! IT FITS PERFECTLY. NOW WE ONLY HAVE TO FIND ONE MORE PIECE BEFORE WE CAN GO HOME TO OUR MOM. THANK YOU, KING RICHARD.

BEFORE YOU GO, WOULD YOU PLEASE READ TO ME THE STORY OF SINBAD? IT WILL HELP ME SLEEP.

Sinbad

SUDDENLY, THERE'S A FLASH OF LIGHT AND THE WATER IN THE BOOK BECOMES REAL.

THE CHILDREN ARE SUCKED INTO THE TIME TUNNEL!

WHOA!!!!!

The Crusades

The Christian knights of Europe fought against the Muslims in several wars known as the Crusades. The Crusades were fought to win Jerusalem, the Holy City, back from the Muslims.

The main weapon in medieval wars was the sword. European swords had straight edges. When the sword was held with its tip pointing downwards, it looked like a cross. Muslim swords had curved edges, and their hilts were often decorated with jewels and beautiful writing.

Saladin and Richard the Lionheart were both fearless leaders in the Crusades. Even though they fought on opposite sides, they had respect for each other. Saladin did, in fact, send King Richard I of England sherbet when he was sick.

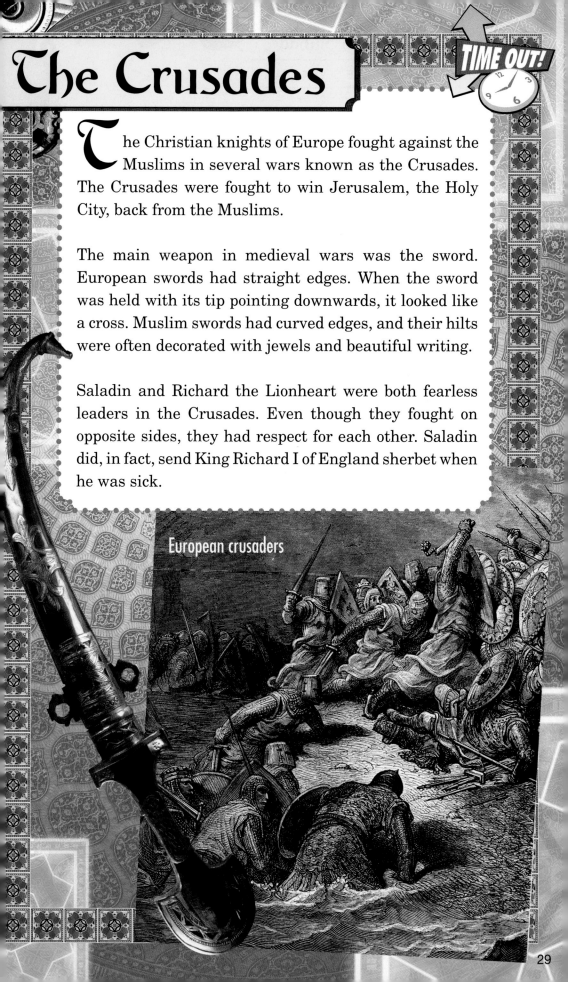

European crusaders

SUDDENLY, AN EVEN LARGER MONSTER – A GIANT EEL – APPEARS.

SHOW ME YOUR SHINY TILE. I WONDER WHY THE THREE-HEADED CREATURE WAS AFTER IT.

WE NEED TO FIND THE LAST MISSING PIECE TO TRAVEL BACK TO OUR TIME — 2006.

I'M GOING TO PICK UP SOME TREASURE I BURIED ON AN ISLAND WHILE ESCAPING FROM PIRATES. MAYBE YOU'LL FIND YOUR MISSING TILE THERE.

GREAT! LET'S GO!

SINBAD'S SHIP REACHES THE ISLAND.

AH, YES. I REMEMBER THIS LITTLE ISLAND. I THINK THE TREASURE IS BURIED OVER THERE BY THOSE TREES.

SUDDENLY, A DARK SHADOW COVERS THE ISLAND.

I THINK IT'S GOING TO RAIN. LOOK HOW DARK THE SKY IS GETTING.

MINA, THAT'S NOT A RAIN CLOUD. IT'S A ... A ....

IT'S A ROC – A GIANT BIRD. WE HAVE TO HURRY! IT MAY SWOOP DOWN AND LOOK FOR DINNER!

WHAT DOES THE ROC EAT?

US!

King Shahryar with his wife, Sheherazade

The Stories of the Arabian Nights

The *Arabian Nights*, sometimes referred to as *1001 Nights*, is a collection of folktales from India, Persia, and Arabia. These stories were retold throughout the Muslim Empire and were very popular.

According to legend, an evil king named Shahryar killed each of his wives after one night of marriage. To stay alive, his last wife, Sheherazade, told him a story that did not end for 1001 nights. Some of the stories we know from *The Arabian Nights* are "Aladdin," "Ali Baba and the Forty Thieves," and "Sinbad the Sailor."

The story of Sinbad is thought to be based on the adventures of Arab sailors who sailed with Admiral Cheng Ho.

IT'S SOME KIND OF EARTHQUAKE.

WHAT WAS THAT?

LOOK AT THAT!

DANGER FROM ABOVE AND BELOW!

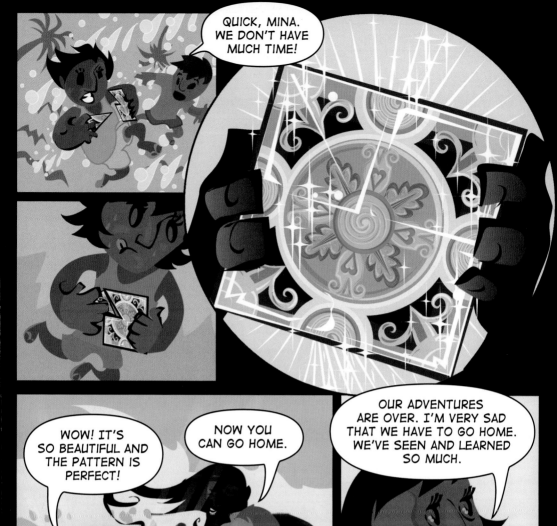

CHILDREN, *HURRY!* YOU MUST GET ON BOARD.

MINA! THE TILE!

WE'LL BE TRAPPED HERE *FOREVER!*

NOT IF I CAN HELP IT!

The Art of Storytelling

The Roc

Storytelling was an art form during medieval Islamic times. Storytellers were welcome in palaces, courts, and market-places.

The Roc (sometimes spelled Rukh) is a giant mythical bird that appears in many Middle Eastern stories. In one of his voyages, Sinbad meets the Roc along with an island that turns out to be a whale! In other stories, he meets dwarfs and narrowly escapes being eaten by a one-eyed giant.

Another famous character in Middle Eastern stories is Hodja. Hodja is a wise man who travels the world facing backward on his donkey. In some countries, he is known as Goha.

In medieval Europe, stories were told about King Arthur and the Knights of the Round Table and about Robin Hood.

The Golden Age

During the Golden Age of Islam, cities such as Baghdad, Timbuktu, and Cairo were centres of learning. In fact, the medieval Muslims were the first to build universities and colleges. The library in Cordoba, the capital of Muslim Spain, had half a million books!

In science, Islamic scholars discovered the principle of the pendulum, and they used it to measure time. In mathematics, Muslims invented the number zero (0) and the decimal system. In the area of medicine, Muslims knew about the infectious nature of diseases, and built hospitals to take care of patients.

Ancient city of Cairo

Both men and women could become doctors, scribes, teachers, and judges.

Muslim scholars translated books from ancient Rome, Greece, India, and China into many languages. They shared this knowledge with many scholars from Europe, which was much less advanced at this time. This learning helped Europe to come out of the Middle Ages.

INDEX